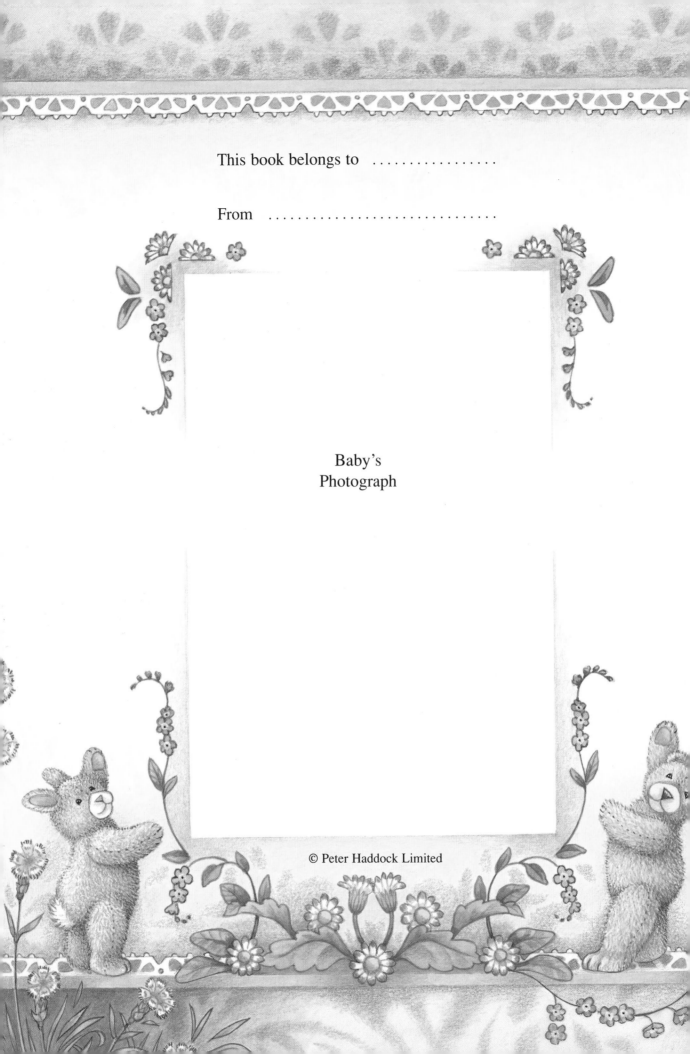

This book belongs to ....

From ....

Baby's
Photograph

BABY
RECORD BOOK

My Arrival

Date . . . .

Time . . . .

Place . . . .

Doctor's name . . . .

Nurse's name . . . .

My Birth Weight . . . .

My Name . . . .

My Birth Sign . . . .

My Birth Stone . . . .

My Appearance

Colour of hair   . . . .

Colour of eyes   . . . .

Complexion   . . . .

Length   . . . .

Circumference of head   . . . .

My First Photographs

Photograph

Photograph

My First Cards

From –

. . . .

. . . .

. . . .

. . . .

. . . .

. . . .

. . . .

. . . .

. . . .

. . . .

. . . .

. . . .

. . . .

. . . .

My First Presents

From –

I Received –

. . . .

Coming Home

I came home on ....

Photograph

My First Outing

I first went out on ....

I went to ....

The weather was ....

I saw ....

Great-Grandfather

Great-Grandmother

Great-Grandfather

Great-Grandmother

Grandfather

Grandmother

Father

Me

Great-Grandfather

Great-Grandmother

Great-Grandfather

Grandfather

Great-Grandmother

Grandmother

Mother

My Christening

I was named . . . .

on . . . .

at . . . .

by . . . .

My Godparents were

. . . .

. . . .

. . . .

. . . .

Photograph

My Progress

My **Weight** at –

1 month	7 months . . . .
2 months	8 months . . . .
3 months	9 months . . . .
4 months	10 months . . . .
5 months	11 months . . . .
6 months	12 months . . . .

My **Height** at –

1 month	. . . .	7 months	. . . .
2 months	. . . .	8 months	. . . .
3 months	. . . .	9 months	. . . .
4 months	. . . .	10 months	. . . .
5 months	. . . .	11 months	. . . .
6 months	. . . .	12 months	. . . .

My **Milk Teeth** appeared on –

	Date		Date
1st tooth	. . . .	7th tooth	. . . .
2nd tooth	. . . .	8th tooth	. . . .
3rd tooth	. . . .	9th tooth	. . . .
4th tooth	. . . .	10th tooth	. . . .
5th tooth	. . . .	11th tooth	. . . .
6th tooth	. . . .	12th tooth	. . . .

I had all my teeth by . . . .

My Health

My **Immunisations** –

. . . .

. . . .

. . . .

. . . .

. . . .

. . . .

. . . .

My **Visits** to the **Doctor**

. . . .

. . . .

. . . .

. . . .

Milestones

	Date		Date
My first smile	. . . .	My first solid food	. . . .
My first laugh	. . . .	I first sat without help	. . . .
I first slept all night	. . . .	I first crawled	. . . .
I first rolled over	. . . .	I first stood	. . . .
My first time in big bath	. . . .	I first walked	. . . .
My first time in big cot	. . . .	My first word	. . . .

My First Lock of Hair

I first had my hair cut on . . . .

My Favourite Toys

Bathtime

Photograph

My Favourite Food

I enjoy eating –

. . . .

. . . .

. . . .

. . . .

. . . .

. . . .

. . . .

I do **not** like –

. . . .

. . . .

. . . .

. . . .

Fun and Games

My favourite activities are

. . . .

. . . .

. . . .

. . . .

. . . .

. . . .

. . . .

. . . .

. . . .

. . . .

. . . .

. . . .

My First Birthday

Photograph of
My First
Birthday Party

Gifts I Received

....

....

....

....

....

....

....

....

People Who Came

....

....

....

....

....

....

....

....

My First Christmas

My age on Christmas Day . . . .

Presents I Received

. . . .

. . . .

. . . .

. . . .

. . . .

. . . .

. . . .

Where Christmas was spent . . . .

Photograph of
My First
Christmas

My First Holiday

Where I went ....

Who went with me ....

....

....

....

Date ....

My age ....

What we did ....

....

....

....

....

Photograph of
My First
Holiday